M000278119

CHINESE BUSINESS
STRATEGIES

ASIAPAC COMIC SERIES

CHINESE BUSINESS STRATEGIES

奇招妙法

Written by
Jiang Wei

Illustrated by
Jiang Wei and Ma Weichi

Translated by
Alan Chong

ASIAPAC • SINGAPORE

Publisher
ASIAPAC BOOKS PTE LTD
629 Aljunied Road #04-06
Cititech Industrial Building
Singapore 1438
Tel: 7453868
Fax: 7453822

First published December 1994

© ASIAPAC BOOKS, 1994
ISBN 981-3029-48-X

*All rights reserved. No part of this publication may be reproduced, stored in a
retrieval system, or transmitted, in any form or by any means, electronic, mechanical,
photocopying, recording, or otherwise, without the prior written permission of the
publisher. If this copy is defective, kindly exchange it at the above address.*

Cover design by Bay Song Lin
Typeset by Unistar Graphics Pte Ltd
Body text in 8/9 pt Helvetica
Printed in Singapore by
Chung Printing

Foreword

Lim Ho Hup is the chairman of Aneka Investment and Management Pte Ltd.
He also acts as the honorary auditor of Singapore Institute of International
Affairs (SIIA) and the treasurer of Singapore National Committee for Pacific
Economic Cooperation (SINCPEC).

Bookshops bulge with numerous business management tomes but few of
these books have managed to explain abstract concepts as entertainingly or as
vividly as this comic book. Although the stories in this book relate more to
entrepreneurship than management, the use of ancient anecdotes to illustrate
business management brings home the point that concepts like initiative,
innovation and adaptability are by no means inventions of the modern
management gurus but universal virtues which can be applied to many
situations.

In addition, I think that the inescapable "Chineseness" about the comics will
be appealing to many. For example, a tale using horses to illustrate the
importance of transmitting information quickly may seem obsolete in the
days of faxes and computers. Nevertheless, the story illustrates rather
colourfully the economic importance of efficient communication and the
value of up-to-date information. Perhaps this is the *raison d'etre* of all comics:
they enable more people to gain insight into complex and abstruse concepts
in a digestible way without having to plough through the more indigestible—
Ricardo's theory of comparative advantage and trade, for example — to gain
similar insights.

I cannot confirm the historical veracity of any of the episodes but I do not
consider this an important issue. Whilst Tang Bohu was a real historical figure
and was known to be harsh in his dealings with pseudo-intellectuals and social
climbers, it is not possible to confirm if this particular incident was recorded
in any other historical tracts. But then, this comic book does not aim to be a
historical text. Rather, it uses a historical setting to teach. As Chinese
entrepreneurship is well-known, there are numerous plausible stories to be

drawn from a Chinese historical setting. To illustrate: it is a historical fact that the ancient city of Hangzhou during the Southern Song era (AD 1127-1280) already had a population of some 300,000 without modern conveniences such as cars, phones, piped water and modern sanitation. That implied a lot in terms of municipal and commercial organization. A sustained period of commerical activities presumably engenders a commercial culture such as would confer the quality of acumen among some of its members. There should be gems of wisdom for those who are willing to explore.

While some may prefer the more erudite-seeming management tomes couched in jargon, I would prefer to say that elegance in diction is no substitute for real understanding. Laozi put it in this way:

> "If you have caught the fish,
>   forget about the fish trap;
>   If you have grasped the concept,
>   forget about the actual wording."

Lim Ho Hup
December 1994, Singapore

Publisher's Note

It is well-known that the Chinese are good businessmen that can thrive even in the most difficult market conditions. What is the secret of their success? *Chinese Business Strategies* brings to light their secret using 10 basic time-tested principles. It is presented in a light-hearted and easy-to-understand manner for those who want a quick insight into success.

In line with our *Strategy and Leadership Series, Chinese Business Strategies* deals specifically with the subject of business management. We hope that it would prove to be useful to businessmen and aspiring entrepreneurs alike.

We would like to thank Ms Jiang Wei and Mr Ma Weichi for the illustrations, Mr Alan Chong for translating this volume, Mr Lim Ho Hup for writing the Foreword, and the production team for putting in their best effort in the publication of this book.

Titles in the Strategy and Leadership series:

The Art of War: Chinese Military Classic
Thirty-six Stratagems: Secret Art of War
Six Strategies for War: The Practice of Effective Leadership
Gems of Chinese Wisdom: Mastering the Art of Leadership
Three Strategies of Huang Shi Gong: The Art of Government
100 Strategies of War: Brilliant Tactics in Action

About the Illustrators

Jiang Wei, a permanent resident of Singapore, graduated from the Attached Secondary Fine Arts School of Central Academy of Fine Arts and University Complutense of Madrid, Spain. Once the art editor of Newton Publisher in Singapore, she is now managing her own company, specializing in organizing art and book exhibitions. Her works include *Hua Mulan, the Ancient Chinese Heroine,* first published in the USA and now available in English, French, Vietnamese, Chinese and Cambodian; *How to Write Chinese,* published in the USA; *Development of A City,* published in Italy; *Four Great Ancient Inventions,* published in Hongkong; *Pictorial Chinese History: The Southern Song Dynasty, The Repentant Bird, The One-Headed Woman,* published in Taiwan; and *The Thirty-six Stratagems,* published in China.

Ma Weichi, born in 1959 in Chengde, Hebei province, China, graduated from the Faculty of Art, Shifan University, in 1985. His many cartoon works and traditional Chinese paintings were selected for national, county and provincial art exhibitions. They have also been published in many domestic and foreign publications. He is a member of the China Artists Association and head of the Chengde Minzu Shifan Advanced Art School.

About the Translator

Alan Chong is a professional translator who undertakes a wide range of Chinese-English and English-Chinese translation assignments from literary works to technical and legal documents. He has translated the following titles in Asiapac Comic Series: *Sayings of Han Fei Zi, A New Account of World Tales, Rainbow Garden, Journey to the West Book I, Journey to the West Book II, Battle Domestica, The Sour Pack, Six Strategies for War, Three Strategies of Huang Shi Gong, Popular Chinese Jokes* and *Chinese Business Strategies.*

Contents

Speed 快

Surprise 奇

Novelty 新

Packaging 妙

Quality 精

Resourcefulness 計

Flexibility 變

Reputation 道

Benefit 惠

Goodwill 情

There were two merchants, Qi Zhao and Miao Fa.

One day, they met at a tea house and started talking about the secrets of doing business.

Tea

How are you?

Hi, Miao Fa, you're so well-informed on the ancient and present ways of doing business.

You flatter me. Ancient and present business approaches seem to differ greatly, but they're invariably based on a 10-word formula.

1

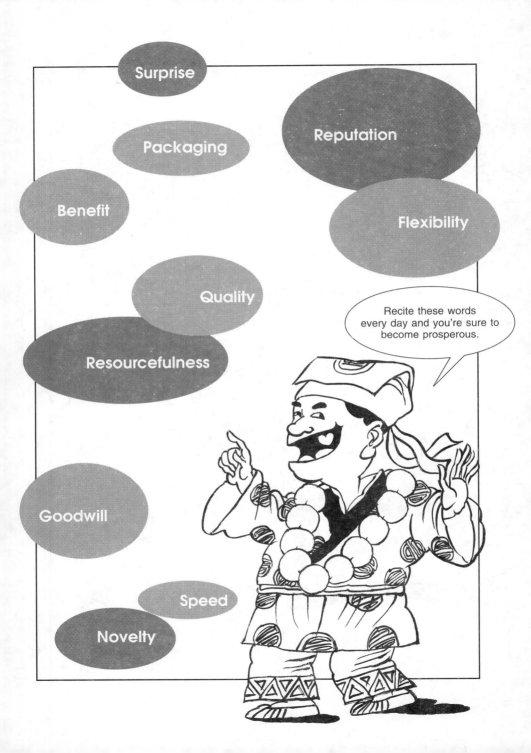

Wise rulers and capable generals are often able to defeat their enemies and achieve outstanding successes because they have prior information on the situation.

– Sun Zi's Art of War

Liu Bao's Business Information Network

5

One year, it rained continuously for five days in Luoyang.

Luoyang

7

8

9

11

The Database Of A Shoe Shop

Zhao Ting was the owner of Nei Liansheng.

After listening to the story, Qi Zhao recalled the story of Nei Liansheng Shoe Shop of the Qing dynasty.

The name, Nei Liansheng, was chosen because it meant having consecutive promotions.

Shop attendants took careful measurements of every customer's feet.

His Excellency's right foot measures... extra-large big toe...

They also recorded the measurements.

We'll send the shoes to you as soon as they're ready, sir.

One day, Zhang Hongsheng, a candidate for the imperial examinations, came to the shop.

With a customer database, Nei Liansheng was able to provide fitting shoes promptly.

Gong Xiji The Early Bird

Gong Xiji of the Spring and Autumn period made a fortune by acting decisively on information.

Soldiers of the Zhu kingdom found that their military uniform tore easily.

Armies at war usually fight in direct confrontation. But those capable of springing a surprise will win. Such tacticians are as versatile as the changes in Heaven and Earth, and as inexhaustible as the flow of a great river.

– Sun Zi's Art of War

Surprise

In addition to speed, an element of surprise is needed in business.

I have a host of stories to tell you in this connection.

The Medicine Shop With A Celebrity's Name

Ancient merchants liked to attract customers with celebrities' names. Xu Jian'an was a merchant during the Qing dynasty.

In his younger days, he was an apprentice in a medicine shop.

I'm going to set up my own medicine shop....

Let's see if there's a suitable shop lot.

23

Tong Jun Medical Hall

By widely seeking folk prescriptions, Xu Jian'an rapidly built up the reputation of his medicine shop.

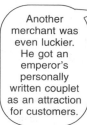

Another merchant was even luckier. He got an emperor's personally written couplet as an attraction for customers.

This is call borrowing a celebrity's name to jack up one's reputation.

The Emperor's Valuable Handwriting

28

29

Couplets Of A Gifted Scholar

Tang Bohu was a leading scholar in Jiangnan during the Ming dynasty.

"Revenue flows in like water; Business flourishes like spring grass."

The new shop was crowded with customers.

32

Emulate the strengths of others, and use their weaknesses for self-correction.

– Lun Yu (The Analects)

Gong Ziqiao Faking An Antique Qin

* a seven-stringed plucked instrument.

36

37

38

Caizhi Zhai, The Celebrated Confectionery

Jin Yinzhi was a confectionery seller during the Qing dynasty.

40

41

42

Kuai Xiang's Movable Sill

A Ming emperor wanted to build a palace.

44

47

48

Unexpected Gain From Good Packaging

Packaging

A man from Chu was selling pearls in Zheng. He made magnolia boxes perfumed with cassia spice, bounded with beads, decorated with red gems and filled with the halcyon's feathers, to put the pearls. A customer bought the box but returned the pearl. He may be said to be good at selling boxes but not pearls.

– Hanfei Zi

Packaging must be attractive and advertisements must be eye-catching. Once, a jewellery merchant saw a fisherman with a huge pearl.

What a huge pearl! What's the price?

50

51

52

53

Soliciting Business By Extracting Gall Bladders Of Live Snakes

56

Before long, Wu Man opened a snake tonic restaurant. He also solicited supplies of live snakes.

I've eaten all kinds of delicacies but not snake meat. I wonder how it tastes like.

Welcome.

Snake meat is inedible!

You were swift and dexterous!

A real master!

Thank you!

This is genuine stuff!

Wu Man punctured the gall bladder, mixed the bile with wine and offered the mixture to customers.

Ha! Ha! Even I am tempted to go and try it!

Wu Man's restaurant became so famous that everyone wanted to go and try his snake tonic.

蛇
玉
滿

Huqingyu Tang's Publicity Blitz

Let me tell you a similar Qing dynasty story.

Huqingyu Tang was a famous medicine shop in Hangzhou.

It was best known for its All-Deer Pill, a tonic preparation made from the Sika deer.

67

68

Huqingyu Tang's publicity blitz was very effective.

With an accurate mould, pure metals, meticulous smelting and the right heating, one can make a superior sword. Without sharpening, it cannot cut a string but after sharpening, it can be used to cut through utensils and kill animals with ease.

– Xun Zi

Tongren Tang Prides Itself On Quality

72

There were more than 40 processes for making the pills; each was carried out rigorously to ensure the best quality for the final product.

Store them for two years to rid them of heatiness before selling. Then they'll have a perfect taste.

The pills are ready.

No wonder Tongren Tang is still famous today!

Qilu Wine, The Superb Brew

Liu Baiduo, a master brewer during the Northern Wei era, was just as meticulous as Tongren Tang in quality control.

It's brewing time again, sir.

Get the cart ready. We'll go together to buy the grain for the brew.

No, I must go with you. The choice of raw material is crucial.

Let me go alone this year. I already know what grain is suitable for brewing.

76

79

Yipin Zhai, The Quality Brush Shop

During the Qing dynasty, Xia Jun'an founded the Yipin Zhai Brush Shop.

I heard that you need a shop assistant, sir.

82

83

85

Acquiring A Piece Of Prize Jade By Damaging It

Some are able to rule their states well because they know how to act at the right moment and have a good sense of priority.

– Guan Zi

91

Several days later, Jian Zhizi held a feast at home.

I'd like to show you a gem.

Wow, fabulous jade!

Magnificent!

93

Slashing Horse Prices By A Trick

95

Lingwu Chu Suppressing Rice Price

102

104

Making A Fortune From Cross-trading of Pigs

Laws are made to take care of the people, and rites are made to facilitate doing things. In ruling a state, a wise man aiming to make the state strong and prosperous need not follow antiquated laws; and as long as it benefits the people, need not adhere to outmoded rites.

– Book of Shangjun

Flexibility

To survive and succeed in the fast changing world of business, the businessman has to stay cool and act according to circumstances.

During the Eastern Han dynasty, only black pigs were raised in the Liaodong area.

108

After travelling for three months, Master Zhou finally arrived in Yanjing.

Yanjing doesn't have black pigs. Why not sell the black ones there and bring back the white ones?

In Yanjing…

Wow, black pigs!

What breed is this? How strange!

I'd like to have two.

Flexibility is a wonderful tool that can help us not only in winning in the face of fierce competition, but also in recouping a loss sometimes.

Ha! Ha!

You've become rich in less than a year. What's your secret?

Give us a tip.

Beating A Cheat At His Own Game

113

114

117

Recovering A National Treasure By A Swop

Towards the end of the Qing dynasty, Patten, a foreign missionary, visited the Baoguo temple in Beijing.

Wow, a 400-year-old masterpiece!

Steal the Goddess of Mercy statuette from the temple for me and this bag of money is yours.

119

Honesty Is The Best Policy

Being trustworthy in minor things helps build up one's reputation. An enlightened ruler should establish a good reputation.

– Hanfei Zi

Reputation

Next comes reputation. A good reputation is indispensable to a successful business.

Huqingyu Tang

The Huqingyu Tang medicine shop has a unique design; its business hall is inside.

Customers have to walk through a 30-metre winding corridor before arriving at the business hall.

Golden Deer Pill

Xingjun Powder

Descriptions of 38 famous medicines are displayed.

Genuine Prices

127

Buying Back A Sick Cow

Meng Xin of the Northern and Southern dynasties was poor despite being a businessman and a farmer.

Bye!

Take care.

One day, he left home for an extended business trip.

We've run out of grain, Mum!

129

* a unit of ancient Chinese currency.

130

Together, they found the man who bought the cow.

I'm sorry sir, this cow is sick.

Sorry, uncle!

I'd like to buy back the cow. Here's 100 *qian*.

You're so honest, sir; 80 *qian* will do.

As Meng Xin's reputation as an honest man spread, more and more people were willing to do business with him.

Tragic End For A Cheat

During the Spring and Autumn period, Yu Fu, a poor man wishing to get out of poverty, consulted a wealthy businessman for tips on doing business.

Lacquer is selling well these days.

So Yu Fu started growing lacquer trees.

Five years later, Yu Fu started to tap the mature lacquer trees.

My brother heard that lacquer is fetching good prices in the Wu state.

He also said that adulterating lacquer with a paste of lacquer leaves could double the profit.

Good idea!

Yu Fu rushed to prepare paste of lacquer leaves.

He arrived in the Wu state with his lacquer.

136

139

140

The reason why a decree is implemented smoothly is that it accords with the people's wishes; and the reason why it is met with resistance from the people is that it goes against their wishes ... so, those who know how to give in order to take have understood a valuable lesson in government.

– Guan Zi

Benefit

Liu Po Clearing The Way For The Benefit Of The Public

143

146

148

Attracting Businessmen By Abolition Of Taxes

Towards the end of the Tang dynasty, the economy of Hunan was badly hit by incessant wars.

I want to turn round the economy here.

Ma Yin was the governor of Hunan.

The tax exemption attracted many traders to Hunan.

153

154

Boosting The Economy By Liberalizing The Timber Market

The Xiaodaiqings were a mountain tribe during the Wanli era of the Ming dynasty.

They frequently plundered villages in Liaodong.

Really? Since we have so much timber, we might as well sell it in Liaodong to make a bundle.

Brother, timber prices in Liaodong are higher than those of gemstones.

Li Hualong was the governor of Liaodong.

157

158

Plentiful supplies quickly brought down timber prices in Liaodong. The timber market was very active.

The active timber market stimulated the horse market.

As more traders came to Liaodong, various industries flourished.

The more you give others,
the richer you'll become;
the more you contribute to
others, the more you'll get
in return.

– Lao Zi

Goodwill

Finally, I'll talk on the importance of goodwill.

Meng Tuo Paying A Fortune For An Obeisance

Zhang Rang was a powerful eunuch during the Eastern Han dynasty.

Many high officials and businessmen fawned on him.

People bearing gifts for him kept streaming to his residence.

163

165

166

In less than 10 days, Meng Tuo had received more than 10,000 taels of gold.

Having built up a name for himself, Meng Tuo was able to expand his business quickly in the capital.

Striking It Rich Through A Letter Of Recommendation

Hu Shiwen was a fabric trader turned art dealer. A poor art appraiser, he lost a lot of money and ended up languishing in Suzhou.

169

171

172

173

Winning By Good Service And Good Public Relations

175

176

177

With sales boosted by direct dealings with the imperial court, Wang Mou's business expanded rapidly.

Donghua

A jealous official discussed with his henchman how to undermine Wang Mou.

One day...

Here are the 200 cases of satin ordered by the Internal Affairs Department.

Open and check!

Strategy & Leadership Series by Wang Xuanming

Thirty-six Stratagems: Secret Art of War
Translated by Koh Kok Kiang (cartoons) &
                    Liu Yi (text of the stratagems)
A Chinese military classic which emphasizes deceptive schemes to achieve military objectives. It has attracted the attention of military authorities and general readers alike.

Six Strategies for War: The Practice of Effective Leadership
Translated by Alan Chong
A powerful book for rulers, administrators and leaders, it covers critical areas in management and warfare including: how to recruit talents and manage the state; how to beat the enemy and build an empire; how to lead wisely; and how to manoeuvre brilliantly.

Gems of Chinese Wisdom: Mastering the Art of Leadership
Translated by Leong Weng Kam
Wise up with this delightful collection of tales and anecdotes on the wisdom of great men and women in Chinese history, including Confucius, Meng Changjun and Gou Jian.

Three Strategies of Huang Shi Gong: The Art of Government
Translated by Alan Chong
Reputedly one of man's oldest monograph on military strategy, it unmasks the secrets behind brilliant military manoeuvres, clever deployment and control of subordinates, and effective government.

100 Strategies of War: Brilliant Tactics in Action
Translated by Yeo Ai Hoon
The book captures the essence of extensive military knowledge and practice, and explores the use of psychology in warfare, the importance of building diplomatic relations with the enemy's neighbours, the use of espionage and reconnaissance, etc.

Forthcoming...
(Asiapac Comic Series)

THE
FAMILY

A
Contemporary
Chinese Classic
Based on
the novel by
BA JIN

Illustrated by Bozong,
Yuqing & Qingguo
Adapted by Gao Tielin & Wang Lijun
Translated by Wu Jingyu
An Asiapac Publication

Forthcoming...

Other Asiapac Titles

ASIA PACIFIC HERITAGE SERIES
A Dream of Red Mansions
Cast Your Chinese Horoscope
Contemporary Architecture in Hong Kong
Contemporary Chinese Fables
Fascinating Tales of Old Beijing
Feng Shui
Folktales of Old Japan
Ghost Stories of Old China
Golden Ox and Other Chinese Comic Tales
Journey to the West
Li Sao - The Lament
Liaozhai Stories of Fox-fairies, Ghosts and Other
Marvels
Ming Shu
Myths of Ancient China
Outlaws of the Marsh
Strange Tales of Liaozhai
Tang Dynasty Stories
"True" Crime Cases from Ancient China
Wisdom Stories

CREATIVE WRITING
Anthology of Chinese Humour
Butcher's Wife
Celebrated Stories by Great Russian Writers
Chess King
Dark Secret and Other Strange Tales
God of Fortune
God of Television
God with the Laughing Face
Heroin Trail
Jokes, Riddles & Proverbs from Asia and the
    Pacific
Legend of Planet Surprise
100 Smiles from Traditional China
Posthumous Son and Other Stories
Shades of Grey
True Story of Ah Q
World's Best "True" Ghost Stories
World's Strangest "True" Ghost Stories
World's Weirdest "True" Ghost Stories

GUIDES & REFERENCES
Concise Japanese-English Dictionary
Legal Status of Singapore Women
Popular Chinese Idioms: Volume 1
Popular Chinese Idioms: Volume 2

《亞太漫畫系列》
智謀叢畫

奇招妙法

編繪：姜巍、馬唯馳
翻譯：張家榮

亞太圖書有限公司出版